GW00642298

SHIRE NATURAL H

BEE ORC

STEPHEN BLACKMORE

CONTENTS

Introduction 2
Bee Orchids and their relatives 2
The British species of *Ophrys* 4
The life cycle of Bee Orchids 7
The pollination of Bee Orchids 16
The ecology of Bee Orchids 19
Bee Orchids and conservation 22
Where to see Bee Orchids 22

COVER: *Flowering spike of Bee Orchid (Ophrys apifera).*

Series editors: Jim Flegg and Chris Humphries.

Set in 9 point Times roman and printed in Great Britain by C. I. Thomas & Sons (Haverfordwest) Ltd, Press Buildings, Merlins Bridge, Haverfordwest, Dyfed.

Introduction

The orchids are a fascinating group of plants. The seemingly infinite variety of their flowers, which are different in shape from those of any other plant, display a dazzling range of complexity in their colouring and the great rarity of many orchids seems to add to their allure.

Orchids have long been considered special plants. The ancient Greeks thought their distinctive paired tubers resembled testicles, which is the literal meaning of the word *orchis* in Greek. They attributed to the tubers the remarkable properties of increasing potency and virility. If the men ate the larger of the two unequal tubers it was thought that they would have male children, whilst if women ate the smaller tubers daughters would result. Similar associations were found in other parts of Europe, where the tubers were known as stones.

During the Victorian era the fascination with orchids grew as the cultivation of exotic species became fashionable. The Victorians had a similar passion for ferns and many wild populations of both kinds of plants were much depleted by collectors digging them up. Today orchids are the basis of a huge commercial cultivation industry, which introduces new varieties, produced by hybridisation, at the rate of over a hundred each month.

Interest in wild orchids has not waned and fortunately awareness of the delicate balance between orchids and their environment, which is so easily imperilled, continues to grow.

Bee Orchids and their relatives

Orchids belong to one of the two largest natural families of flowering plants, the Orchidaceae. This family contains fifteen to twenty thousand species and thus includes almost a tenth of all the known flowering plants in the world. A more precise figure of their numbers cannot be given because many orchids have been named more than once by different botanists, a fact which does not come to light until a detailed study of the members of a particular part of the family is made. Furthermore, the opinion of botanical experts varies over what should be deemed a distinct species and what a mere variety. Since the orchids are a family in which many species exhibit variations in colouring or form, the question of what status to give them is particularly important. Added to these difficulties in numbering the orchids is the certainty that many members of the family not yet known to botanical science remain to be discovered, especially in the remote and underinvestigated regions of the world. For many of these the destruction of their habitat will lead to their extinction before they are ever observed or studied. Only the Daisy family, Compositae, exceeds the Orchidaceae in number of species. Both are 'natural' families in the sense that they are at once distinguishable from all other plant families by a number of obvious and distinctive characteristics. Other plant families are recognisable only by careful study of rather technical differences.

The orchids belong to the group of flowering plants known as the Monocotyledons. Other familiar members of this group include the grasses, sedges, lilies, amaryllises and irises. All of these typically have long narrow leaves with parallel veins and the parts of their flowers arranged in groups of three or multiples of three. In this they differ from the Dicotyledons, which have net-veined leaves and flower parts mostly in numbers other than threes.

Most of the characteristics of the orchids concern their flowers, which are unusual in many ways. In the great majority of orchids each flower has only one fertile pollen-producing stamen. This stamen, which represents the male part of the reproductive system of the flower, is at least partly joined to the female part of the flower, forming a unique structure known as the column. The overall symmetry of the flower is bilateral rather than radial. This means that there is only a single plane through which the flower

2

THE CLASSIFICATION OF BEE ORCHIDS

CLASS — *ANGIOSPERMAE*
The flowering plants

SUBCLASS — *MONOCOTYLEDONAE*
about 60 families
including: ——————

DICOTYLEDONAE
about 260 families

FAMILY — *ORCHIDACEAE*
the Orchid Family
about 20,000 species in
3 subfamilies

SUBFAMILY — *APOSTASIOIDEAE*
with 2 genera

ORCHIDOIDEAE
with 740 genera
in 4 tribes

CYPREPEDIOIDEAE
with 5 genera

TRIBE — *ORCHIDEAE*
mainly terrestrial
orchids, photosynthetic

NEOTTIEAE
mainly terrestrial
orchids, saprophytic

VANDEAE
mainly tropical
epiphytic orchids

EPIDENDREAE
mainly tropical
epiphytic orchids

GENUS — *OPHRYS*
40 species,
4 in Britain including: ——————

SPECIES — *APIFERA*
Bee Orchid

VARIETIES — *TROLLII*   *BICOLOR*   *CHLORANTHA*

can be divided into two equal mirror images. Radial flowers, such as those of buttercups or daisies, have two or more planes of symmetry. The showy part of the flower, which is known as the perianth, has six segments. The outer three are frequently greenish and may be called sepals and the inner three are more colourful and may be called petals. Sometimes the distinction between petals and sepals is not made, in which case all six perianth segments are termed tepals. The central petal of the orchid flower is highly modified in shape and is known as the lip or labellum. The labellum is the most distinctive, and also the most variable, part of the orchid flower. It is usually divided into several lobes, is often strikingly coloured and may have a nectar-producing extension or spur.

The pollen of orchids is also unusual in that it is formed in special structures called pollinia which consist of masses of pollen grains adhering together. In almost all other families of plants the pollen grains are released singly or, less commonly, in small groups of four or more pollen grains. Curiously the mem-

bers of one other family, quite unrelated, the Milkweeds or Asclepiadaceae, also have pollinia. In both families the pollinia are associated with adaptations for specialised methods of pollination and thus they provide an excellent example of convergent evolution, by which similar structures arise in unrelated plants but function in the same way. Most of the peculiarities of orchid flowers relate to the complex and intriguing methods of pollination found in the family. These have captivated many naturalists, including Charles Darwin, who wrote an important textbook on the subject.

The seeds of orchids are also different from those of other plants in that they are microscopic structures made up of only a few cells. They are produced in vast numbers, often more than a million in a single pod, and dispersed by the wind.

The unique combination of characteristics which occurs in the Orchidaceae provides a theme which is found, in innumerable variations, throughout the family. The great majority of orchids are found in the tropical regions of the world, where many grow as epiphytes, high up

3

on the branches of forest trees. A smaller number of orchids extend into the colder parts of the world and to the harsh conditions prevailing on high mountains.

The Bee Orchid, *Ophrys apifera*, belongs to a European genus, or group of closely related species, which includes about forty members. They are distributed from Europe to north Africa and western Asia but the greatest number of *Ophrys* species are to be found in the Mediterranean region, where there are also numerous subspecies and varieties.

Ophrys belongs to a subfamily of Orchidaceae known as the Orchidoideae, as do most British orchids. This is one of the three subfamilies recognised by most authorities on the orchids and is characterised by possession of a single fertile stamen and pollinia with elongated stalks which are enclosed in folded pockets. Another subfamily, the Cypripedioideae, has two fertile stamens per flower and is represented in Britain by one species, the Lady's Slipper Orchid. This plant has been collected almost to the point of extinction and now survives in only a single location in Yorkshire. The same species is still to be found elsewhere in Europe, where it has suffered a similar decline.

Recognising members of the genus *Ophrys* is quite easy. The flowers are borne in a loose spike rather than in a dense head as in most of the native British orchids. The labellum is distinctly fleshy and is covered with velvety hairs and, most important of all, it lacks a nectar-producing spur. A feature of *Ophrys* species which is not normally seen is that they have two spherical or globular tubers below ground level. Similar tubers do occur in some other orchids but most have elongate, cigar-shaped or palmately lobed tubers. The shape of tubers is of interest in deciding to which group a species belongs and in determining the relationships between groups of species but it would never be consulted in identifying an individual.

The genus *Ophrys* is divided into four sections containing groups of closely related species and three of these occur in Britain, where they are represented by a total of four species. In the past species status was given to at least one of the varieties of Bee Orchid so that older books may refer to five or more native species of *Ophrys* in Britain.

The British species of *Ophrys*

The Bee Orchid is the most commonly occurring member of its genus in Britain and of the other three the Fly Orchid, *Ophrys insectifera*, is most likely to be encountered. The Fly Orchid is a plant of calcareous soils which grows in marshes, grassland and, in particular, along the margins of woods. The Late Spider Orchid, *Ophrys fuciflora*, is similar to the Bee Orchid in the appearance of its flowers but is very much rarer and, in Britain, occurs only in a few areas of chalk downs in Kent. The Early Spider Orchid, *Ophrys sphegodes*, also resembles the Bee Orchid and is rather rare although having a wider distribution, from Kent through Sussex and Hampshire into Dorset.

The four species are distinguishable by differences in the colour of their flowers. In the Fly Orchid and Early Spider Orchid the sepals are green or greenish yellow and rather like small leaves. The labellum of the Fly Orchid is narrow, three-lobed with the central lobe slightly indented, and is a deep reddish brown with a white or bluish central blotch. That of the Early Spider Orchid is broad, only weakly lobed and purplish brown with yellow markings. The sepals are a pale rose-pink in the Bee Orchid and Late Spider Orchid but the two species differ in details of the labellum. The Late Spider Orchid has a flattened, roughly rectangular labellum which ends in a small upright appendage. The labellum of the Bee Orchid is convex rather than flattened, more deeply lobed, rounded and ends in a small pointed appendage which is tucked backwards under the labellum.

The differences by which the four native British *Ophrys* species may be

Plate 1 (above). *The habit of the Bee Orchid. They are mostly found as scattered individuals amongst the other plants of chalk grassland although small clusters may sometimes be found.*

Plate 2 (above, right). *The lowest flowers of the Bee Orchid open first, whilst those at the apex are still in bud. The number of flowers may be as few as two or as many as a dozen. Here both unopened buds and ripening ovaries are present.*

Fig. 1. *Species of British Ophrys (from left to right): Fly Orchid; Early Spider Orchid; Late Spider Orchid; Bee Orchid.*

5

Fig. 2. *Ophrys*
flowers, front
and side views

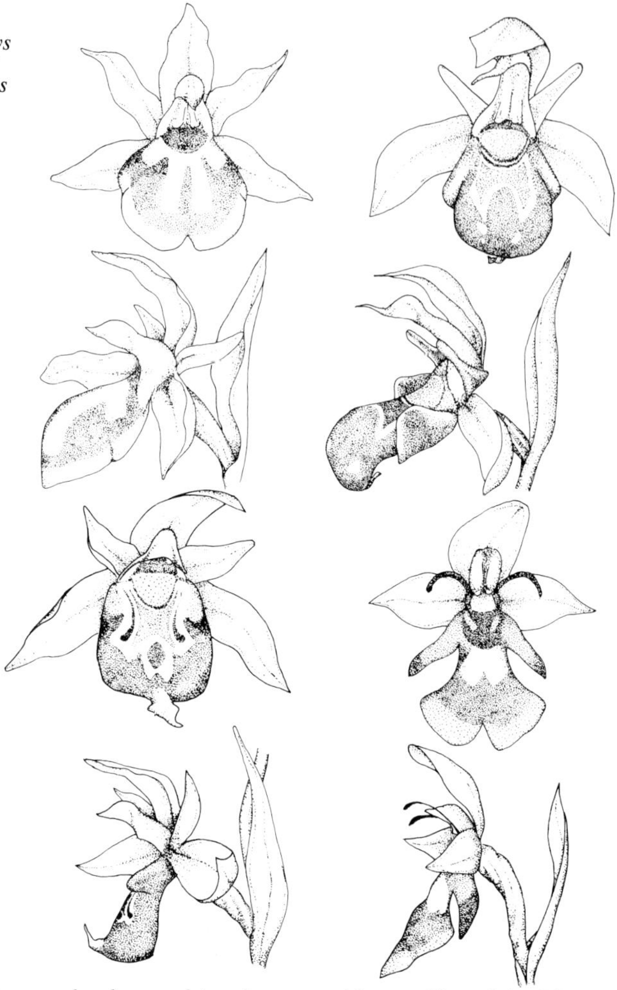

Early Spider
Orchid.

Bee Orchid.

Late Spider
Orchid.

Fly Orchid.

distinguished may also be used to place them into the various sections into which the genus is divided. The Bee Orchid itself belongs to Section *Apiferae*, a name of Latin derivation which means 'bee carrying', as does the specific name *apifera* of this species. All members of this section share the characteristics of a convex, three-lobed labellum and pink sepals. The two species of spider orchid belong to Section *Araniferae*, the name of which is also Latin and means 'spider carrying'. The species of this section have a flattened labellum which is not deeply lobed and has an upward-turned appendage. The sepals may be either green,

white or lilac-pink. The Fly Orchid belongs to Section *Ophrys*, which is characterised by a long flattened labellum with three lobes and greenish sepals.

It is interesting that the section and species names of these orchids emphasise their resemblance to living creatures. The same is true of their common English names and those of many other orchids. It seems that the striking and complicated shapes of orchid flowers have always conjured up images in the mind and these are reflected in such names as Lizard Orchid, Man Orchid and Lady's Slipper Orchid.

	BEE ORCHID O. apifera	EARLY SPIDER ORCHID O. sphegodes	LATE SPIDER ORCHID O. fuciflora	FLY ORCHID O. insectifera
Sepal colour	pink	green	pink	green
Lateral petal colour	pink to greenish	pink to greenish	pink to brown	brown
Lateral petal shape	flattened to rolled	± flattened	± flattened	tightly rolled
Labellum shape	strongly 3-lobed	weakly 3-lobed	strongly 3-lobed	strongly 3-lobed, centre lobe forked
Labellum appendage	curled under	absent	curled up	absent
Labellum colour	purplish to dark brown	purple/brown	maroon to dark brown	reddish brown
Labellum markings	yellow spots, sometimes H-shaped	bluish H-shaped mark bordered with yellow	blue to maroon marks bordered with yellow	central bluish blotch
Flowering months	June-July	April-June	June-July	May-July
Flowers per spike	2-6 (rarely 12)	2-8	2-7	4-12
Height of stem	15-45 cm	10-35 cm	10-35 cm	15-60 cm
Hybrids formed		O. × pseudoapifera	O. × obscura	O. × hybrida

O. × albertiana

The life cycle of Bee Orchids

SEEDS AND GERMINATION

The seeds of the Bee Orchid, like those of other orchids, are minute and powdery. They each consist of an embryo made up of only a few cells surrounded by a flattened veil-like wing or integument, which aids their dispersal by wind. The seeds are therefore quite unlike the elaborate structures found in more familiar plants. Most seeds contain reserves of stored food, in the form of fats or oils held in the cotyledons, the fleshy embryonic leaves which emerge when the seed begins to germinate. In large seeds such as beans or maize the cotyledons and embryonic root and shoot can easily be seen if a seed is split open. These structures consist of thousands of cells and are the product of growth of the original embryo. Such seeds also have a thickened outer protective layer which protects the delicate embryonic tissues until suitable conditions for growth trigger off the germination of the seed.

The seeds of orchids are very different: they contain no reserves of food to give them a start in life and consequently cannot begin to germinate unassisted. The extreme reduction in size of the individual seeds makes it possible for fruits of orchids, which are relatively small capsules, to contain vast numbers of seeds. The capsules of Bee Orchids contain between six thousand and ten thousand seeds. This represents a fairly typical number of seeds for the capsule of a British orchid but seems modest when compared to the estimated four million seeds in each of the very large capsules of the Central American Swan Orchid, *Cynoches chlorochilon*. The capsules are strongly ribbed or ridged and are at first

7

Fig. 3. *Bee Orchid life cycle.*

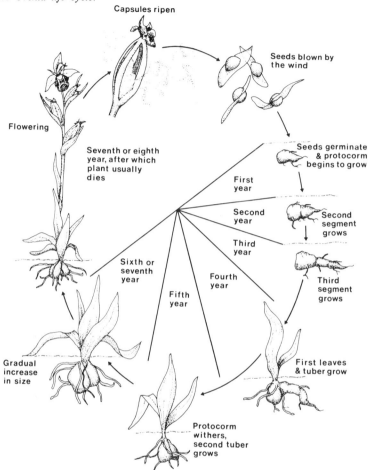

Capsules ripen

Seeds blown by the wind

Flowering

Seventh or eighth year, after which plant usually dies

Seeds germinate & protocorm begins to grow

First year

Second year

Second segment grows

Third year

Sixth or seventh year

Fourth year

Fifth year

Third segment grows

First leaves & tuber grow

Gradual increase in size

Protocorm withers, second tuber grows

green in colour. Later, as the capsules slowly ripen over a period of a few months, they dry out, becoming brown and eventually splitting open to reveal the straw-coloured powdery or mealy seeds.

Carried by gusts of wind, the seeds may be dispersed quite widely from the parent plant. They can succeed in growing only if certain rigorous conditions are met. Bee Orchids, like the majority of their family, are very selective about the degree of acidity, or pH, which they can tolerate. They will only germinate on basic soils, which have a high pH, and

mostly occur on such calcareous bedrocks as chalk or limestone. The seeds will also germinate successfully in the dry, well drained soils which form on the landward sides of sand dunes. It has often been noted that Bee Orchids and other species of *Ophrys* favour sites such as disused chalk pits or quarries where the soil has been disturbed at some time in the past.

Whilst the type of soil is very important to the germination of orchid seeds, there is an even more important factor. The seeds are unable to germinate without the assistance of certain types of fungi which live in the soil and provide the sustenance

8

Plate 3. *The typical colour markings of a Bee Orchid flower. The labellum, in particular, may vary in colour but generally has deep red blotches outlined in white or pale yellow and a number of other yellowish markings.*

Plate 4. *A small plant of Bee Orchid growing amongst Bird's Foot Trefoil (Lotus corniculatus). The Bee Orchid has non-resupinate flowers, which appear upside down compared to normal plants. In some populations such plants are quite common even though this position of the flowers is less favourable for self-pollination.*

which enables the tiny orchid embryo to begin its slow growth. The relationship with the fungus is a complicated and precarious one, which begins simply as a parasitic invasion or infection of the orchid seeds by the microscopic fungal growths. The fungi which form this association with orchids belong to the genus *Rhizoctonia*, whilst other kinds of fungi form associations with the roots of other plants, including heathers and pines. For germination to be successful the orchid seed must retaliate against the invading fungus and begin to absorb nutrients from it. A perilous balance is then struck between the continuing attack of the fungus and the ability of the orchid to survive this and at the same time gain nutritional benefit from it. In nature many orchid seeds fail to germinate because they are overwhelmed by the fungal onslaught.

With nutrients from the fungus the germinating orchid begins to grow, at first forming an elongated underground structure called a protocorm or mycorrhizome. For several years this interaction continues, with the protocorm adding a new segment each year but with no evidence of the plant above ground. The growth of an orchid seedling is very different from that of most plants, which grow very rapidly at first in order to reach the sunlight and begin to produce new food reserves. After three or four years the orchid protocorm gradually becomes like a more normal plant, producing a few slender roots and one or two small leaves during the summer. Although painstakingly slow, this rate of growth is quite rapid compared to that of some orchids. The Lady's Slipper is perhaps the slowest of the native British species, taking fifteen to eighteen years to grow from seed to flowering. For the Bee Orchid several years of gradual growth follow the production of the first leaf. The leaves die back in winter, having boosted the food reserves of the plant during the summer by the normal energy-producing process of photosynthesis. These reserves are transported below ground and stored in small spherical tubers.

After five to eight years of growth the Bee Orchid has two fully developed tubers and a fibrous root system. The protocorm is no longer apparent, having been gradually consumed in contributing to the growth of the plant. By this stage the orchid is no longer reliant on its association with the fungus to survive and may be almost entirely free of infestation. In this respect *Ophrys* species differ from the many orchids which remain more or less dependent on fungi throughout their lives. The extreme examples are species

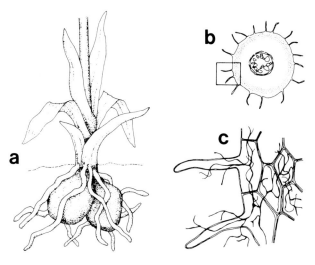

Fig. 4. *Underground parts of the Bee Orchid: (a) root system and tubers, with the basal leaves; (b) section through a root showing root hairs, conducting tissues in the centre and mycorrhizal zone with fungal hyphae (stippled); (c) detail of area marked in (b), showing root hairs which take up water; fungal hyphae are also shown.*

such as Bird's Nest Orchid *(Neottia nidus-avis)* or the much rarer Ghost Orchid *(Epipogium aphyllum)* which never develop large leaves or the pigments needed to carry out photosynthesis. These plants are saprophytic, deriving their nutrition, via their fungal intermediaries, from the leaf litter in which they grow.

The year in which a Bee Orchid flowers depends upon its having accumulated sufficient reserves for the energy-consuming processes of growing an inflorescence and producing flowers. Commercial cultivators of orchids can slightly improve upon the achievements of nature with certain orchids. Species of *Ophrys*, for instance, can be grown without mycorrhizal fungi if the seeds are nourished instead by growing them in sterile conditions on a special nutrient jelly. In this way flowers can be produced in five years, equalling the best growth achieved in the wild.

THE FLOWERING OF BEE ORCHIDS

In Britain Bee Orchids are frequently monocarpic, that is they produce a flowering shoot only once and then die, having consumed all their reserves of energy. Some plants do survive to flower again in subsequent years, especially those growing in favourable localities or in years when climatic conditions have been ideal. Further south in Europe individual Bee Orchids usually flower several times over a period of years, sometimes missing a year and carrying out purely vegetative growth. This difference in behaviour emphasises that *Ophrys* is a distinctly Mediterranean genus and that the Bee Orchid is at the northern edge of its range in Britain. The majority of British orchids are capable of flowering repeatedly over a number of years.

In the autumn before flowering the Bee Orchid produces a small rosette of leaves, tightly pressed against the ground to protect against the cold of winter. In April or May a single upright inflorescence grows from each plant. This is a spike of between two and six flowers, although rarely as many as twelve flowers may occur in a single spike. The size of the inflorescence varies considerably in length, depending, mainly, on the habitat. In very exposed sites such as the short turf of chalk downs the inflorescence may be a mere 5 centimetres (2 inches) long. Plants in the same populations but in more sheltered positions, perhaps between scrubby patches of Dogwood or Hawthorn, may well reach 30 centimetres (12 inches) or more. Along the length of the spike a few leaves occur. These are ovate to lanceolate in shape and distinctly larger towards the base of the spike than higher up.

Each bud has a leafy bract below it which is rather longer than the bud itself. The bracts and buds are both held vertically at first but the buds gradually curve downwards as they open. At the same time they undergo a remarkable process called resupination, which occurs in most members of the Orchidaceae. This involves the development of a 180 degree twist in either the ovary or the flower stalk. As a result of this twisting the labellum is the lowest petal when the flowers open, the reverse of its position in the bud. In the Bee Orchid the twist occurs in the pedicel not the ovary and so the ridges which run along the length of the ovary are straight. In some *Ophrys* species the twist occurs in the ovary so the ridges themselves are curved. Occasionally resupination fails to take place and this results in one or more of the flowers opening upside down. The same phenomenon is sometimes reported in other species, for instance the Pyramidal Orchid *(Anacamptis pyramidalis)*, which on rare occasions produces entire spikes of flowers which have opened without inverting. The flowers of the Bog Orchid *(Hammarbya paludosa)* appear not to have twisted at all but undergo a 360 degree rotation, which brings them back to their starting point. The Ghost Orchid *(Epipogium aphyllum)* is one species which never undergoes resupination but regularly flowers upside down. The process of resupination is an important one because it brings the labellum into the correct position for it to form a landing stage for the insect visitors which pollinate the flower.

The flowering season of the Bee Orchid varies considerably throughout its geographical range, depending upon the

11

Plate 5. *An exhausted bee crawls over a Bee Orchid inflorescence, neither searching for nectar nor detaching any of the pollinia. This visit by a bee is coincidental and any small plant might have provided a place for the bee to recover.*

Plate 6 (below, left). *After flowering the petals fade but remain attached to the ripening pods.*

Plate 7 (below, right). *The Fly Orchid (O. insectifera) grows amongst other shade-tolerant plants on the woodland floor.*

Plate 8 (above, left). *Seen in detail, the flower of a Fly Orchid has the same parts as a Bee Orchid but the labellum is strikingly different. The insect-like appearance is highly distinctive.*

Plate 9 (above, right). *Although the Early Spider Orchid (O. sphegodes) has a shorter flower spike than the Bee Orchid and greenish petals the similarities with its close relative are obvious.*

Plate 10. *A group of Early Spider Orchids growing in closely cropped turf of chalk grassland.*

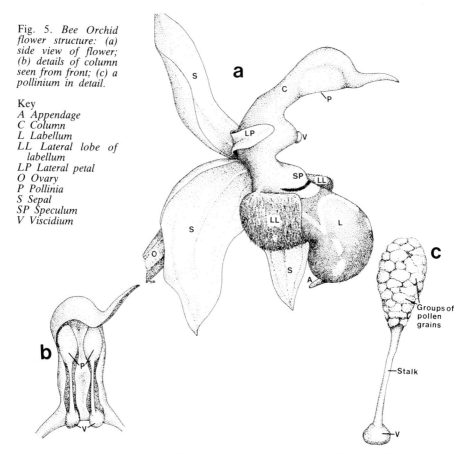

Fig. 5. *Bee Orchid
flower structure: (a)
side view of flower;
(b) details of column
seen from front; (c) a
pollinium in detail.*

Key
A *Appendage*
C *Column*
L *Labellum*
LL *Lateral lobe of
labellum*
LP *Lateral petal*
O *Ovary*
P *Pollinia*
S *Sepal*
SP *Speculum*
V *Viscidium*

Groups of
pollen
grains

Stalk

latitude. In the southern part of its range, in Cyprus and Greece, the flowers open as early as April. In Britain they usually bloom in June but in favourable years, after a mild spring, they may be in flower late in May. In the south of England, where Bee Orchids are most abundant, most plants will have finished flowering by the end of June and only a few open flowers will be found in July. In the north of England, and in shadier localities elsewhere, they may continue late into July. As with other species of orchid, the lower buds are first to open and those at the apex of the spike are last.

DETAILED STRUCTURE OF THE BEE ORCHID FLOWER

The Bee Orchid is one of the most beautiful British orchids and the resemb-

lance of the individual flowers to a bumble bee is quite striking.

The sepals are all of equal size, about 10-15 millimetres (½ inch) long, and taper gradually from the base to the tip. The central sepal usually curves forward over the column of the flower, whilst the other two are often slightly reflexed. Although the sepals are usually pale pink lightly veined with green, they may sometimes be white or uniformly pale green. Forms with pale green sepals could be confused with the Early Spider Orchid except for the differences in the labellum of the two species. The lateral petals are much smaller than the sepals and are usually tightly rolled into a cylindrical shape so that they appear narrow and bluntly tapered. Their colour is usually the same as that of the sepals and they

14

project upwards and slightly forwards at the sides of the column. The lateral petals of the Fly Orchid occupy a similar position but are much more delicate and have a strong resemblance to the antennae of an insect. Those of the Bee Orchid are sometimes suggestive of antennae but much less dramatically so.

The labellum contrasts sharply with the sepals and lateral petals in its three-lobed shape and distinctive colouring. The predominant colour of the labellum is a deep red or purplish brown and its texture is that of velvet. At the top of the labellum is an almost hairless rounded region known as the speculum, which is a rich orange or light reddish brown. The speculum (which means 'mirror') of many *Ophrys* species is shiny as in the Fly Orchid or the southern European Mirror Orchid *(Ophrys speculum)* and resembles the reflective surface of an insect's wings folded above its body. In the Bee Orchid the speculum is outlined by a dark, often almost black border and surrounded by a series of irregular yellow lines or dashes. These often form an H-shaped mark on the labellum. At the apex of the labellum is a narrow, pointed tooth-like appendage which lies folded back behind the labellum and when seen from the side looks rather like a spur. The Bee Orchid does not have a nectar-producing spur, unlike the majority of orchids. The side lobes of the labellum are curiously shaped conical or triangular structures which curve upwards and then abruptly down at each side of the flower. They are much hairier than the rest of the labellum and may be uniformly brown or have a yellowish blotch.

The column is light green and projects forwards from the flower, tapering to a curved point. It is often described as resembling the head of a duck and this impression is especially strong when the column is viewed from one side. To see the detailed structure of the column it is necessary to use a hand lens or a strong magnifying glass, but the flowers should be examined without picking them. At the base of the column is a rounded knob-like stigma region, which is the area upon which pollen grains can germinate. Above this protrude the two sticky bases of the pollinia. The pollinia themselves are, at first, enclosed in pouches but later their long stalks curve forwards, bringing the pollinia into contact with the stigma.

VARIETIES AND HYBRIDS

Whilst this description applies to the majority of Bee Orchids, the flowers are more variable than those of most plants. There is great diversity in the pattern and colour of the markings of the labellum and if a large group of Bee Orchids is found together it will soon be seen that they are not all identical. Some of the most unusual versions have been given distinct names. The Wasp Orchid, for example, is so different that it not only has its own common name but is regarded by some botanists as a distinct species, *Ophrys trollii*. Most authorities now agree that the Wasp Orchid is only a variety of Bee Orchid and use the botanical name *Ophrys apifera* var. *trollii*. The labellum of the Wasp Orchid is long and narrow, tapering to a tooth-like point which is not curved backwards. It differs in colour also, being a pale yellow with large dark brown blotches. The principal locality of the Wasp Orchid is Gloucestershire, where it grows in grassland on the limestone hills of the Cotswolds, but it is also sometimes found in parts of Dorset, Oxfordshire and Wiltshire. Newly opened Bee Orchid flowers may sometimes be mistaken for Wasp Orchids because, when the petals first unfold, the apical appendage has not yet folded under the labellum. Occasionally Bee Orchid plants are found in which some of the flowers have the typically folded appendage and others resemble the Wasp Orchid. The genus *Ophrys* is considered by botanists to be an example of a group of species which is still undergoing evolutionary differentiation and variations which arise, like the Wasp Orchid, may eventually become so distinct as to be generally accepted as distinct species.

Other varieties lack the full range of colour pigments found in the flowers of typical Bee Orchids. A pale greenish yellow form, which may be encountered, very rarely, throughout most of the range of the Bee Orchid, is known as var. *chlorantha*. It has sepals which are white, veined with green, a greenish column and a rather narrow yellowish green labellum.

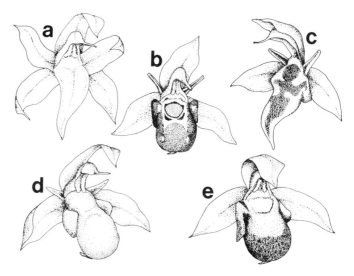

Fig. 6. *Bee Orchid flower variations: (a) variety with sepal-like petals; (b) typical form; (c) O. apifera var. trollii, Wasp Orchid; (d) var. chlorantha, a semi-albino form; (e) var. bicolor, a brown and green form.*

Another widely distributed but rare coloured variety is var. *bicolor*, in which the labellum has a pale greenish speculum and upper parts merging gradually into a deep brown towards the apex and its appendage. A rare variety found in parts of Sussex, and sometimes in Europe, has all the petals, including the labellum, resembling the sepals in shape and coloured a pale pink.

In addition to these unusual varieties of Bee Orchid, there also occur, although very rarely, natural hybrids between Bee Orchids and other *Ophrys* species. A hybrid is a cross between two species of plants, which can occur only if pollen is transported from one plant to the stigma of the other, germinates and fertilises the ovules. Generally hybrids can occur only between plants which are quite closely related, since otherwise the sets of chromosomes in the fertilising pollen and the ovules may be unable to combine and divide successfully to produce embryonic cells. In nature there are additional barriers, such as differences in flowering season or in pollinating agents, which prevent hybrids occurring. Plant breeders often bypass these normal barriers to produce new hybrid crosses which may be more desirable in some respects than the parent plants.

The pollination of Bee Orchids

Pollination is the process by which pollen grains are transferred to a receptive stigma and many features of flowers represent adaptations to the different ways in which they are pollinated.

Many flowering plants, including grasses, sedges, plantains and many British trees, are pollinated by wind. This is a chancy process which requires enormous numbers of pollen grains to be shed into the air, causing hay fever in people sensitive to them. Only a minute proportion of these pollen grains ever reach a suitable stigma, and the rest are wasted. The flowers of wind-pollinated plants are usually green and far from showy.

Bright colouration in flowers is usually a sign of pollination by insects, or birds in tropical regions. Insects use flowers as an important source of food in the form of nectar or pollen but, in the process of gathering the food from one flower after another, they frequently transfer pollen on their bodies. Since the feeding behaviour of insects is relatively constant they provide a reasonably reliable delivery service for pollen compared to the risks of entrusting it to the wind. Both insects and flowers benefit from this interaction and in many cases close partnerships have evolved, over millions of years, between one group of insects and particular flowers. Many flowers, such as the Dandelion and its relatives, are open to insect visitors of every kind and their flowers attract beetles, butterflies and bees, amongst others. The more restricted the range of insects which visit a flower the more precise a pollinating agency the insects may provide, if they are attracted in sufficient numbers. The construction of many flowers is designed to favour one kind of insect at the expense of all others. Flowers of the Pea family, Leguminosae, are constructed in such a way that the anthers and nectaries are enclosed by the petals and are therefore out of reach of most insects. When a bee of the correct size lands on the flower the petals fold back exposing nectar and showering the visitor with pollen. When flowers of this family, such as clover, are in season the bees in the area tend to specialise in visiting them and are almost perfect pollinators.

In the Orchidaceae elaborate mechanisms to insure pollination by a particular kind of insect reach their peak. The differences between orchids and all other flowering plants except the milkweeds (Asclepiadaceae) is that they contrive, in various ways, to attach entire pollinia containing thousands of pollen grains on to the body of an insect visitor. The insect then delivers far more pollen grains to the stigma of a subsequently visited flower and when these germinate thousands of fertile seeds can be produced. This method of pollination is consequently essential to the production of the vast numbers of seeds found in an orchid capsule.

Most orchids are adapted to a particular kind of insect, as a brief look at the pollination of some common British orchids will show. The Twayblade *(Listera ovata)*, which is probably the commonest orchid in Britain, is pollinated by short-tongued insects such as beetles and flies, which visit the flower to drink nectar. As the insects crawl up the long narrow labellum following the central groove in its surface, which contains the nectar, they come at last into contact with the rostellum, the rounded region above the stigma. When this happens, a drop of liquid is suddenly and forcefully exuded which rapidly hardens like glue and fixes the pollinia on to the insect's back. At the next flower more pollinia may be cemented on to the insect or, if the flower is at a slightly later stage, the stigma will brush against the back of the insect and may detach several pollinia.

The Pyramidal Orchid *(Anacamptis pyramidalis)* has its nectar at the end of a long, hollow spur about 1 centimetre (⅜ inch) long and is visited mainly by moths and butterflies, which have sufficiently long tongues to reach the nectar. The entrance to the spur is narrow and when the proboscis of the insect is fully inserted the bases of the pollinia, which are fused together into a ring, lock tightly around it. The butterfly or moth then flies away from the flower with a pair of pollinia attached to its proboscis. As the pollinia dry out in the air their stalks gradually curve forwards so that when the insect inserts its proboscis into another flower the mass of pollen grains are perfectly positioned to contact the stigma.

Bizarre though such pollination mechanisms may seem, they are far surpassed by those of *Ophrys* species. The Bee Orchid poses something of a riddle, for in Britain it is rarely visited by insects of any kind. Butterflies occasionally settle on the flowers, especially the Marbled White *(Melanargia galathea)*, which is on the wing during the flowering season of the Bee Orchid, but the orchid does not produce any nectar and the butterflies do not seem to look for any. The answers to the riddle of Bee Orchid pollination can be discovered by observing this and other *Ophrys* species further south in their range. It then becomes apparent that the striking resemblance of the flowers to insects is central to their method of pollination. Male wasps or small bees are attracted to *Ophrys* species, and at first it was thought that they landed simply because they mistook the flower for a possible mate. Much careful research has revealed that the male insects are indeed deceived by the *Ophrys* flowers but in a much more

17

subtle way. The labellum of each *Ophrys* species gives off a complex scent which, although virtually undetectable to the human nose, exactly duplicates the attracting substances called pheromones which female insects release to attract males. To attract a mate of the same species, each kind of wasp or bee produces a slightly different scent, to which only males of the same species respond. To deceive the male insects an orchid must duplicate the exact ingredients but in so doing it limits itself to a single bee or wasp species as its pollinator, an arrangement that works well if the insect abounds.

The male insects emerge from their pupae before the females and immediately begin seeking a female to mate with. At the same time the *Ophrys* flowers come into bloom and attract the males. It has been shown that the sensitivity of the male insects is such that they can detect and locate the flowers even when they are concealed from view. The appearance of the flower is not, therefore, vital in first attracting the insect but once the insect reaches the vicinity of the orchid its resemblance in shape and colour and the hairiness of the labellum is enough for the male insect to try to mate. During this attempted mating, which is known as pseudo-copulation, the sticky viscidia at the ends of the stalks of the pollinia attach themselves to the insect's body.

Bees belonging to the genus *Eucera* pollinate the Bee Orchid and both species of Spider Orchids. Spider Orchids seem to attract a wider range of insects, including bees of the genus *Andrena* to the Early Spider Orchid and species of *Tetralonia* to the Late Spider Orchid. The Fly Orchid attracts wasps of the genera *Gorytes* and *Argogorytes* in exactly the same way and, in view of its relatively wide distribution, probably represents the best British species in which to try to observe pseudo-copulation. This requires great patience but carefully and quietly watching a freshly opened population of Fly Orchids may be rewarded.

In Britain, however, the correct species of *Eucera*, which visits Mediterranean Bee Orchids, is lacking. From the occasional hybrids between Late Spider Orchids and Bee Orchids it is apparent that the bees which pollinate the Spider Orchid are sometimes attracted to the Bee Orchid as well. Without the presence of its favoured pollinator how can the Bee Orchid survive in Britain? Chance visits by other kinds of bee might provide the answer but they do not. If one watches bees at work foraging in chalk grassland where Bee Orchids are in bloom it is quite remarkable how rarely they ever alight, even fleetingly, on a Bee Orchid and yet how thoroughly they visit every Thyme, Stemless Thistle or Valerian. It has been shown that there is a reason for this too. Apparently the bees mistake the Bee Orchid flower for a flower upon which a bee is already feeding and in these circumstances their natural behaviour is to move on and find another flower. This has been demonstrated by placing a Bee Orchid flower in amongst the flowers of popular nectar-producing species usually favoured by bees, with the result that bees ceased their visits. Having lost its southern European pollinator, the appearance of the Bee Orchid deters other species of bee from taking their place. There is some evidence that newly emerged bees are less set in their ways of behaviour and in their ability to recognise the best food-producing flowers and so may sometimes unwittingly visit Bee Orchids. Bumble bees have been seen to land momentarily on Bee Orchid flowers and this may have been the explanation. An exhausted bee has been watched crawling up and down a Bee Orchid spike for fifteen minutes or more without once coming close to the sticky viscidia and removing the pollinia.

Fortunately the Bee Orchid has a solution to its plight. If the flowers remain unpollinated then they eventually pollinate themselves. Self-pollination is quite widespread amongst plants of northern latitudes, where insects may be fewer in kinds or in numbers. It has one drawback in that it does not lead to a mixing or exchange of genetic material between plants as cross-pollination does and this exchange is known to encourage vigour in the offspring. Self-pollinated plants also tend to preserve and pass on any unusual varieties which arise, whereas in cross-pollinated plants these are

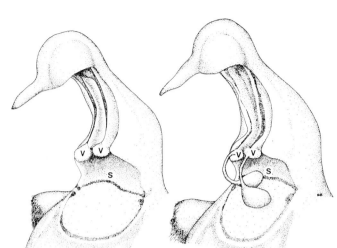

Fig. 7. Bee Orchid self-pollination. Soon after the opening of the flowers the pollinia are still enclosed in pouch-like folds, the sticky viscidia (V) are exposed and cross pollination may take place (left). Later (right) the pollinia fall forward, their viscidia remain in place and the pollen masses contact the stigma (S).

usually lost because the typical form tends to reassert itself in later generations. This is the reason why Bee Orchids have so many colour varieties which maintain themselves in the wild.

Other self-pollinated orchids in Britain include the rare Dune Helleborine (Epipactis dunensis) and the Green Flowered Helleborine (Epipactis phyllanthes). The latter, like the Bee Orchid, is a highly variable species with at least five named varieties in different parts of Britain and in its different habitats. For the Bee Orchid self-pollination is accomplished very easily. The pollinia simply fall forward, whilst remaining attached by their viscidia, and dangle in front of the stigma. If one looks closely at a Bee Orchid spike which has several flowers open it is very probable that the older ones will be seen to have pollinated themselves whilst the upper flowers still wait in vain for the visiting Eucera bees.

Once the pollen masses come in contact with the stigma they begin to germinate. Each pollen grain produces a microscopic tube which grows through the tissues of the ovary and carries a male sex cell, or gamete, to fertilise a female ovule. The ovary is very narrow, resembling a flower stalk before fertilisation, but afterwards, as the embryos mature into

seeds, it gradually becomes larger. For a while the withered remnants of the flower remain attached to the apex of the green pod but eventually they fall away as the pod ripens and turns brown. Finally the sides of the pod split open and the seeds are dispersed by gusts of wind. Of the thousands which are produced only a few will survive to reach maturity as flowering plants.

The ecology of Bee Orchids

The growth and reproduction of Bee Orchids and their intimate dependence upon fungi have been described previously. These details of the lives of the species have important implications for their ecology.

Ecology is the branch of biology which is concerned with the study of the relationships between a plant or animal species and the environment in which it lives. The environment is simply the conditions, for example of light, soil or drainage, in which the plant species lives. Some species are able to thrive in a wide range of environmental conditions and

19

Plate 11 (left). *Side view of a Bee Orchid flower prior to self-pollination.*

Plate 12 (right). *Bee Orchid flowers showing the mechanism of self-pollination. The flower above has its pollinia enclosed within the column whilst the slightly older flower below has pollinia which have fallen forwards and effected self-pollination.*

consequently are found in several different kinds of habitats. A habitat is an area such as a wood, a salt marsh or a peat bog in which a particular set of environmental conditions prevails.

Most species of orchid show marked preference for one, or perhaps a few, habitats. The common Twayblade *(Listera ovata)* is not only the commonest and most widespread of British orchids but also the most tolerant of environmental conditions and can be found on chalk downs, amongst bracken and heathers, in woods and copses or along shady lanes. Twayblade is particularly unusual in that it flourishes on either acidic peaty soils or basic soils of limestone and chalk. The vast majority of orchids favour one or other type of soil and this is the most important factor affecting their distribution. The most significant difference between the two extremes of soil types seems to be the presence or absence in the soil of calcium salts, which if too abundant can inhibit the uptake of other mineral salts by plants. Those species which prefer basic soils, rich in calcium,

are known as calcicoles (meaning living on calcium) and those which prefer acidic soils, where calcium is lacking, are known as calcifuges (meaning calcium avoiding).

The Bee Orchid and allied species provide good examples of calcicoles and are most abundant in areas with chalk or limestone bedrock. The two spider orchids are both restricted to chalk downs in the south of England, where they grow only in open grassland. Both were formerly more widespread and suitable habitats still exist elsewhere in Britain. The Early Spider Orchid, the most widespread of the two, was known from a locality in North Wales in the nineteenth century and in the twentieth century grew in Oxfordshire, Northamptonshire and Cambridgeshire. The much rarer Late Spider Orchid has not been found outside Kent in the twentieth century although it was once to be found in Dorset, Suffolk and Surrey, roughly the present distribution of the Early Spider Orchid.

The Fly Orchid is the most widespread British *Ophrys* species and occurs in parts of Ireland, Scotland, Wales and England, although it is much more common in the southern half of its range. It is the most northerly of all *Ophrys* species, its range extending into Norway and Sweden. Despite its widespread occurrence in many places where the soil is suitable, it is not often encountered. This is partly because it is an inconspicuous plant which may easily be overlooked. Unlike the other British *Ophrys* species, it is quite tolerant of shade and is most commonly found in the margins of woods. The Bee Orchid is sometimes found just inside a wood but often such instances are explained by the relatively recent colonisation of an area of former grassland by trees.

The Bee Orchid, although less widely distributed than the Fly Orchid, is the *Ophrys* most frequently seen. It has been found in Scotland but is evidently extremely rare there. Its abundance increases towards the south of England. Although a calcicole, the Bee Orchid is not entirely restricted to chalk or limestone soils and may also be found on well drained clay soil and on the landward side of stabilised sand dunes. It grows on dunes in short turf which resembles that of chalk downs and includes many of the same species.

Bee Orchids also have a preference for places where the ground has been disturbed by quarrying or the building of embankments. Continuous digging of the soil prevents them from becoming established or continuing to survive but soil which has been disturbed may be better drained and it is probably this which encourages the growth of Bee Orchids. Such well drained soils are rather deficient in nutrients because the rain water filtering through the soil dissolves and rapidly transports away the soluble salts from the soil. Orchids are able to survive such conditions because the mycorrhizal fungi which infect the seed and spread through the growing protocorm enable the orchid to extract sufficient nutrients to survive. Many of the other plants which have mycorrhiza, such as heather, grow in mineral-deficient soils. In the same habitat as the Bee Orchid other plants use different strategies to overcome the shortages. Members of the Pea family such as Bird's Foot Trefoil (*Lotus corniculatus*), Horseshoe Vetch (*Hippoc-*

repis comosa) and Kidney Vetch (*Anthyllis vulneraria*), in common with others of their family, have root nodules which contain micro-organisms capable of extracting nitrogen from the air and making it available to the plant.

The porous nature of the well drained soil not only makes it deficient in mineral nutrients but also makes it likely that the topsoil will be very dry. Rain falling on chalk downs soon drains away into the bedrock and only plants which can survive drought will live. For many orchids the underground tubers contain a reservoir of moisture which will protect the plant from desiccation and this is certainly true for the Bee Orchid. However, the main defence of the Bee Orchid against drought is not to appear above ground during the hottest and driest part of the year.

Late in the autumn Bee Orchids produce a small rosette of leaves, flattened against the ground to conserve moisture and to protect against cold. The rosettes help to build up reserves of energy so that an inflorescence can be produced the following year. Even as the flowers are in full bloom the leaves begin to wither, blackening at the tips and then gradually shrivelling as the fruits begin to ripen. By the time the pods open there is little or no trace of green remaining on the plant. Since most British Bee Orchids flower only once this process marks the end of the life of the plant. If the growing season has been an exceptional one the leaves may have produced enough energy for the plant to survive. Most plants, however, are monocarpic and flower only once and this explains the erratic appearance of Bee Orchids. More than any other member of their family, they may be abundant in one locality and then virtually absent in subsequent years. Alternatively they sometimes appear in large numbers where they have not previously been seen. It is these bountiful years that lead to the description, found in many books, of the Bee Orchid as a common plant. Such terms of abundance are strictly relative and although the Bee Orchid is not nearly so rare as the Military Orchid (*Orchis militaris*) or the Red Helleborine (*Cephalanthera rubra*) it is hardly a common species.

Bee Orchids and conservation

Orchids, perhaps more than any other group of wild flowers, have suffered a great decline in numbers during the past two centuries. Two main reasons for this can be identified, and both relate to human activities. Firstly, orchids have often been picked either simply because of their appealing flowers or as specimens by collectors. To pick even a single Bee Orchid flower can drastically reduce the number of seeds set in a locality since the plant is monocarpic and, unlike most British orchids, will not set seed again the following year. Similarly if Bee Orchids are dug up when in flower for transplanting to a garden they are unlikely to thrive there and will not, in any event, flower a second year. Since this is not widely known, the orchids continue to be transplanted, illegally, into gardens.

The second factor which has restricted the occurrence of the Bee Orchid has been the destruction of suitable habitats for them to grow in. Although Bee Orchids will eventually return to a site which has been excavated or quarried they cannot tolerate agricultural chemicals, and changes in agricultural practices have contributed to their demise. It may at first seem contradictory that the chalk downland where Bee Orchids are most abundant is itself a man-made habitat. It has, however, taken thousands of years of tree felling and of grazing by sheep to create the open grassland. On shallower slopes much of the chalk downland has now been ploughed up as arable land because sheep farming is less profitable. Downland which has suffered no greater change than the removal of grazing livestock gradually reverts to hawthorn, dogwood and whitebeam scrub and ultimately to beech or ash wood. For plants of short turf, such as the Bee Orchid, the right balance between grazing and the development of scrub is vital.

The Bee Orchid is in need of conservation because it has been over-collected and because suitable habitats are disappearing. It is not one of the great rarities which merit nature reserves to act as special sanctuaries, such as those in which the Lady's Slipper and the Military Orchid cling to their remaining British footholds. It is one of the many specialities of the British countryside which needs consideration by those who find it, who may look but not pick it, and which on a broader level needs the maintenance of suitable habitats. Many prime areas of chalk downland are now mainly grazed as a conservation measure. Sheep are often transported temporarily to graze on a site, such as the slopes of Box Hill in Surrey. In some areas local conservationists have resorted to careful mowing to maintain a short turf and to clearing scrub by hand to maintain the open habitat. With the decline in sheep farming the rabbit has become an increasingly important herbivore and contributes to the maintenance of grassland.

The Wildlife and Countryside Act affords the protection of law to all wild flowers, including Bee Orchids, but a growing appreciation of the value of wildlife offers more hope in the long term.

Where to see Bee Orchids

Anyone who lives in England, Wales or Ireland may be fortunate enough to find Bee Orchids, especially if they visit an extensive area of chalk or limestone. Without doubt such places as the South Downs, the Chilterns and the Burren of Ireland are the best places to look for Bee Orchids and many other orchids. Elsewhere Bee Orchids may be found quite readily on stable sand dunes, for example, along the coasts of South Wales or North Devon. Often the best remaining habitats have been made nature reserves and these are the best places to look. It is best to contact the local county naturalists' trust, or other conservation groups, for advice on where to see Bee Orchids

Fly Orchid.   Bee Orchid.

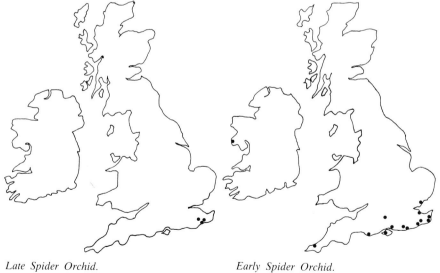

Late Spider Orchid.   Early Spider Orchid.

Fig. 8. The distribution of orchids in the British Isles, based on records since the 1930s.

23

because access to many sites of rare plants is carefully controlled.

This is not always the case and many good localities, especially those on chalk and limestone hills, are popular picnic sites and viewpoints. They are visited by large numbers of people every year, many of whom will not notice the orchids and other interesting plants that grow there. Two good areas of chalk downland owned by the National Trust are Box Hill in Surrey and Watlington Hill in Oxfordshire. Bee Orchids may be found at both, some years in large numbers. A careful search is necessary since, although the flowers are showy and spectacular, they merge into the background remarkably well. When one Bee Orchid is at last found others seem to spring into view nearby.

In exposed sites the Bee Orchids may be of very reduced stature; on windswept escarpments few plants may exceed 10 centimetres (4 inches) in height, with inflorescences of only two to three flowers. It can take a careful search to find the plants, even when visiting the precise spot where they appeared in previous years. In some localities Bee Orchids are amongst the points of interest on a nature trail. This is the case, for example, at one of Britain's finest localities for orchids, the Warburg Reserve not far from Henley-on-Thames, which is run by the Berkshire, Buckinghamshire and Oxfordshire Naturalists' Trust. Here both Fly Orchids and Bee Orchids may be seen, with a host of other chalk downland and woodland plants.

To find the unusual variants of the Bee Orchid is much harder and requires systematic searches of many localities. The Wasp Orchid, in Gloucestershire, may be more easily located than some varieties since it has a definite geographical distribution.

Finally, local libraries can provide the information, in the form of local county floras, which will enable Bee Orchids to be tracked down.

FURTHER READING

Clapham, A. R., Tutin, T. G., and Warburg, E. F. *Flora of the British Isles.* Cambridge University Press, 1962.

Davies, R., Davies, J., and Huxley, A. *Wild Orchids of Britain and Europe.* Chatto and Windus, The Hogarth Press, 1983.

Dupperrex, A. *Orchids of Europe.* Blandford Press, 1961.

Ettlinger, D. M. T. *British and Irish Orchids, a Field Guide.* Macmillan Press, 1976.

Keeble-Martin, W. *The Concise British Flora in Colour.* Ebury Press, 1965.

Nilsson, S. *Orchids of Northern Europe.* Penguin Nature Guides, Penguin Books Ltd, 1979.

Ross-Craig, S. *Drawings of British Plants, Part XXVII.* G. Bell and Sons, 1971.

Summerhayes, V. S. *Wild Orchids of Britain.* Collins New Naturalist Series, Collins, 1968.

ACKNOWLEDGEMENTS

Photographs are acknowledged as follows: T. Cope, plates 7 and 10; P. Lund, cover, plates 1, 2 and 11; B. Tebbs, plates 8 and 9. All other illustrations, are by the author.